Adam had a new car.

He saw a car on television.

It looked like his car.

Adam had an idea.

He went to the flour bin.

He put flour on the car.

He dropped the car.

'Oh no!' said Adam.

He looked in the flour.

He couldn't find the car.

The bin fell over.

The flour went everywhere.

Mum was cross.

Adam was sorry.

"You may be slow," said Benny
when he came to collect Bobby.
"But you're quick at making friends!"

Next morning
when Bobby went to school,
all the other cars said
what a good flying saucer he was.

They all wanted the little bubble car
to join in their games.

All the children in Brummingham
paraded in fancy dress.
Their families clapped and cheered.
It was wonderful.

But the best bit was when the spacemen
and the flying saucer won first prize.

Benny made sure
that all the cars
were neatly parked,
and the show
began.

Everyone stopped
and stared at the
flying saucer and
the little spacemen.

A minute later Bobby was ready.
He loved his new wings!

Benny went ahead
to show the cars
from the driving school
how to drive slowly.

"Easy!" said Mike
and he set to work.

The two little spacemen started to cry.

"I know," said Benny.
"Bobby can be your flying saucer!
Mike, can you fix
the rocket wings on Bobby?"

Mike jumped down with his toolbox.

"Can you fix our rocket?" said the children.

"Not in time for the show," said Mike,
looking at his watch.

"Look out!" shouted Benny.
But it was too late.

The car in front bumped into the rocket
and smashed it to bits.

Luckily the children were safe.

They were going so fast
that they didn't notice
two little spacemen
pulling their rocket.

Suddenly all the cars
from the school
raced out of the gates.

Beep! Beep! Beep!

"They're all going to the show and I can't keep up."
"You may be slow," said Benny, "but you're really
special. You're the only bubble car in the whole of
Brummingham."

Benny found Bobby all by himself in a corner.

"What's the matter, Bobby?" asked Benny.

"Nobody likes me because I've only got three wheels," said Bobby sadly.

They were all in fancy dress.

They looked very excited.

By the time Benny and Mike
set off to collect Bobby,
the streets were full of children.

"Hello, Benny,"
said Mike.
"We're getting ready for the fancy dress show."

"That's nice," said Benny.
"I told Bobby we'd take him after school."

When Benny got back to Smallbills Garage
Mike was helping some children
turn their pedal car into a police car.

"Oh yes!" said Bobby,
cheering up at once,
and he drove bravely
through the school gates.

"I don't want to go to school
with all those big cars," said Bobby.

"You'll be fine," said Benny.
"And just think of the fancy dress show
we're going to see when school's over."

It was Bobby the bubble car's
first day at driving school.
His friend Benny
was going to take him there.

First published in Great Britain in 2000
as a Dolphin Paperback
by Orion Children's Books
a division of the Orion Publishing Group Ltd
Orion House, 5 Upper St Martin's Lane, London WC2H 9EA

Text copyright © Willy Smax 1998, 2000
Illustrations copyright © Keren Ludlow 1998, 2000

The right of Willy Smax and Keren Ludlow to be identified
as the author and illustrator respectively of this work has been asserted.

A catalogue record for this book is available from the British Library
Printed in Italy
ISBN 1 85881 716 1

BENNY
and the Bubble Car

written and illustrated by

Keren Ludlow and Willy Smax

Published in the UK by Scripture Union

207-209 Queensway, Bletchley, Milton Keynes, Bucks, MK2 2EB

ISBN 978 1 84427 256 3

First edition 2007

Editorial Director Annette Reynolds

Editor Nicola Bull

Art Director Gerald Rogers

Pre-production Krystyna Kowalska Hewitt

Production John Laister

Wave hello

Welcome, welcome.
Now you're home safely,
Back home from prison with Peter.

Call, call!
Someone has heard you.
Wait at the door with Peter.

Cup hands around mouth

Knock on the door

Knock, knock!
Knock very loudly.
Knock on the friends' door with Peter.

Quick, quick!
Find the way safely.
Go to the friends' house with Peter.

Run on the spot

Look all around

Look, look!
Where is the angel?
Look all around you with Peter.

Walk and point

Follow, follow.
Follow the angel
Right past the soldiers with Peter.

Wrap your arms around

Wrap, wrap,
Wrap your cloak round you.
Put on your sandals with Peter.

Jump, jump!
A light and an angel!
Wake up and jump up with Peter.

Jump up

Sleep, sleep.
Shut your eyes tightly.
Sleep in the prison with Peter.

Head on hands

Hands together

Pray, pray.
Please God be with him.
Ask God to help our friend Peter.

Shake wrists

Rattle, rattle.
Chained up in prison,
Hear the chains rattle with Peter.

March, march.

Peter's arrested.

March with the soldiers and Peter.

March on the spot

Knock on the door
with
Peter

Marjory Francis and Chris Saunderson

Knock on the door
with
Peter

AN ACTION RHYME BOOK